The Story of a Baby

THE STORY OF A BABY

ILLUSTRATED BY THE AUTHOR

Marie Hall Ets

THE VIKING PRESS   NEW YORK

Acknowledgement

I want to thank Loyola University School of Medicine in Chicago for its beautiful collection of human embryos, which furnished material for many of these drawings.   M. H. E.

612.6   1. Reproduction
         2. Sex instruction

The Story of a Baby

In the beginning there was something so small that only good eyes could have seen it. It was smaller than a seed of hay that flies like dust in the wind. It was smaller than a grain of salt from the shaker, or a grain of sand from the beach.

But this speck was an egg. And within the egg was a particle of stuff as old as life—stuff passed on and on from so long ago that nobody knows from what it started, nor when, nor how, nor why. It was a portion of that stuff from which had grown the early men who lived in caves. It was a portion of that stuff from which had grown the great-

great-great-great-grandmothers and the great-great-great-great-grand-
fathers, and the great-great-grandmothers and the great-great-grand-
fathers, and the great-grandmothers and the great-grandfathers. It was
a portion of that stuff from which had grown the mother herself.

Too small to be seen at all, this particle of stuff had lain hidden away inside the mother since before she was born. From other particles had grown a young brother and a sister. But nothing much had happened to this one until now. Now the mere speck of an egg that grew around it was ripe and moved on through a tube in the mother. But as it moved it met a different kind of particle of that stuff as old as life—one that came from the father. Too small to be seen at all, the new particle pushed its head into the soft round egg and joined the other one inside. And as they touched, something happened—something no one in the world can understand: The stuff in the egg became a new life. It was a life too small to be seen at all, but a life that was going to be a baby. And long before it was a baby ready to be born, there would be hidden away within it a portion of that stuff from which it grew—that stuff of life, which could grow more babies and more babies and more babies, in years and years and years to come. Nobody knows how many. And nobody knows for how long.

A LIFE TOO SMALL TO BE SEEN AT ALL

Now the scientists with their microscopes have watched millions of eggs of all sizes and sorts in which new life has begun. That is why they can say that we all started out inside of our eggs in much the same way—whether we are now whales, or tadpoles, or people, or mice. (But eggs

which are going to be tadpoles are many times larger to start with than eggs which are going to be whales, or people, or mice; because creatures who grow outside of their mothers must have enough food stored up in their eggs to last them until they are hatched, and they must have

extra coverings to protect them.) The scientists say that whenever that stuff in an egg, which they call a cell, becomes a new life it starts dividing. First the one cell divides, making two. Then the two cells divide, making four. And the four cells divide, making eight. And so they go on and on, making more cells and more cells and more cells—tiny round cells too small to be seen, but all clinging together like the bubbles of soapsuds or foam.

And so when the cell which was going to be a baby became a new life, it divided and divided and divided until the mere speck of an egg was full of tiny round cells too small to be seen, but all clinging together like the bubbles of soapsuds or foam. And while the cells inside were dividing, the mere speck of an egg moved on through the tube in the mother. And she did not know that it was there. Soon it came to a cavity where there was plenty of room. Here it stopped and, like a seed carried by the wind, it buried itself in the wall. For here it would stay and grow until it was a baby ready to be born.

Now the outside of the egg had disappeared on its way through the tube and in its place had come a sac, like a house or a cocoon, for the new life to grow in.

It was a house with no windows or doors—a house smaller than a grain of salt from the shaker, or a grain of sand from the beach. But this was a house that could grow, and a house that was going to have roots.

So the house grew and the tiny round cells like bubbles inside had room to grow too. They changed their places, and sizes, and shapes. They pressed together, and crowded, and pushed. They made layers like paper that doubled and folded. And then they began to unfold. And as they unfolded there appeared, as if by magic, the things they were making. There came a sac like a veil or a balloon filled with water for the new life to float in, so that nothing could hurt it as it grew. And there came another sac holding the yolk from the egg, to feed the new life until it could grow from its roots. And between the water sac and the yolk sac, like a bit of cloud, but too small to be seen, was the embryo itself—the part that was going to be a baby.

At first as the embryo grew, in its speck of a house with no windows or doors, it seemed to be making a sponge. But it wasn't to be a sponge. And it went on changing, turning into something else as it grew.

And the third week passed. Now the embryo's house was nearly as large as the seed of an apple, but the roots that grew out like moss all around made it look like a burr. And the embryo itself, in the water sac inside, was large enough to be seen. It was as large as the tail of this comma (,). And it looked like a comma made of cloud. There was a lump where its chin should be. That was its heart getting ready to beat. It had no head and no legs and no eyes and no mouth. It had only a heart and a tail. And its tail grew in sections like a worm. So now it seemed to be making a worm. But it wasn't to be a worm. And it went on changing, turning into something else as it grew.

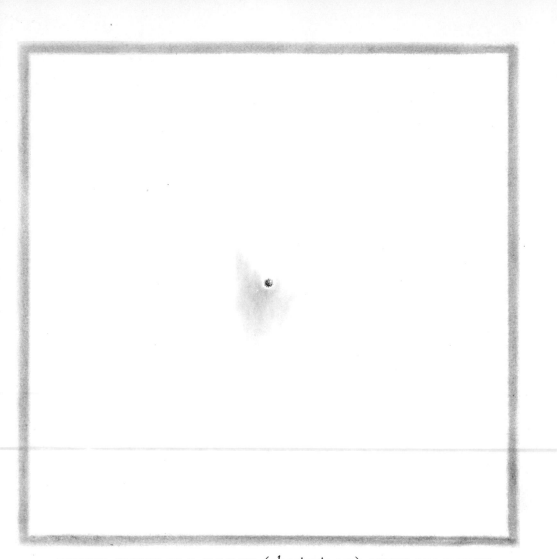

THREE-WEEK-OLD HOUSE (*chorionic sac*) WITH ITS ROOTS

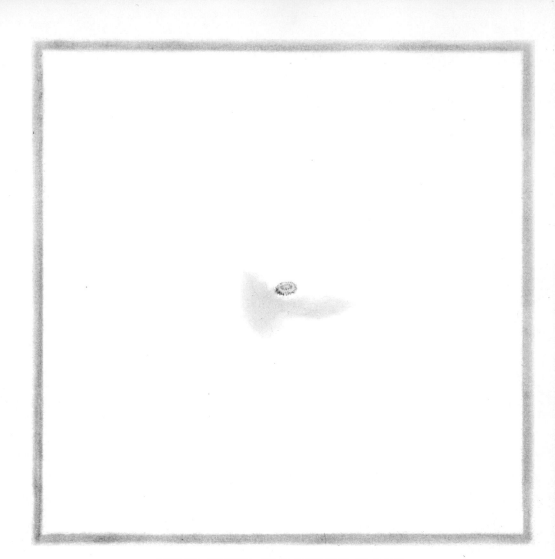

FOUR-WEEK-OLD HOUSE CLOSED

For the next few days the heart of the embryo twitched. Then it started to beat. And now one end of the embryo had grown into a head and on the sides of the head appeared bumps which were buds for its eyes, and hollows which were going to be the insides of its ears. On the

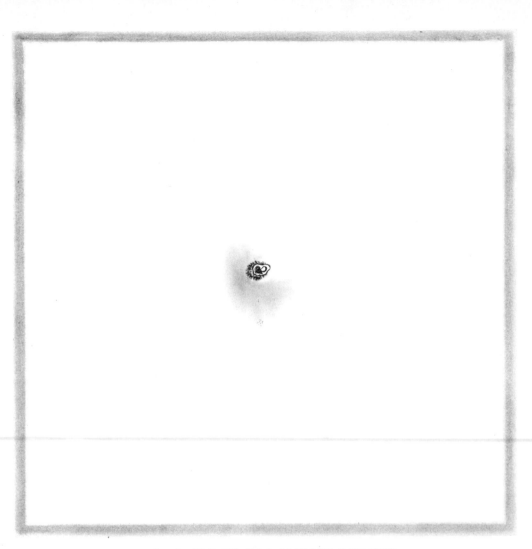

FOUR-WEEK-OLD HOUSE OPENED

front of the head, where it leaned on the heart, a hole burst through to the hollow inside and that was the beginning of a mouth. And on each side, where a neck should be, were dents like the gill slits of a fish. So now the embryo seemed to be making a fish. But it wasn't to be a fish. And it went on changing, turning into something else as it grew.

FIVE-WEEK-OLD HOUSE CLOSED

The fifth week passed. Now the embryo's house was as large as a dandelion in bloom. And like a seed inside, the embryo itself was as large as a kernel of rice, or a kernel of wheat. But it was all curled up in the water sac with its head almost touching its tail. And now other new things were appearing. Half-way down toward the embryo's tail appeared bumps which were buds for its arms. Then further down still there appeared two more, which were buds for its legs. And inside had come buds

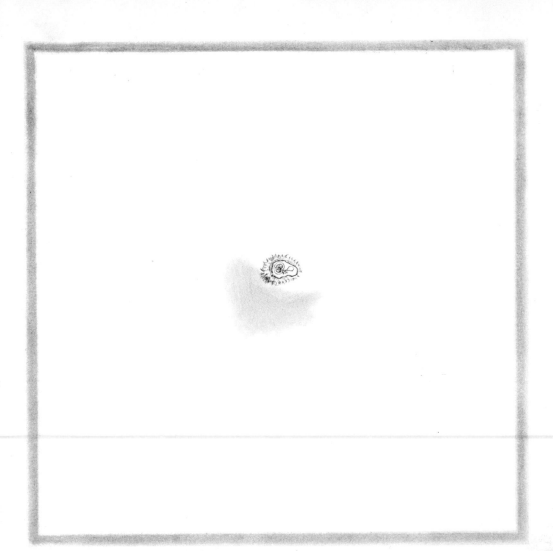

FIVE-WEEK-OLD HOUSE OPENED

for its lungs, and for many other things that it would need. And although it was no larger than a seed, already there lay hidden away within it a portion of that stuff from which it grew—that stuff of life from which could grow more babies and more babies and more babies, in years and years and years to come.

As the embryo grew, the water sac and the house grew too. But the sac of food was disappearing, for now the roots on its house could bring it whatever it needed.

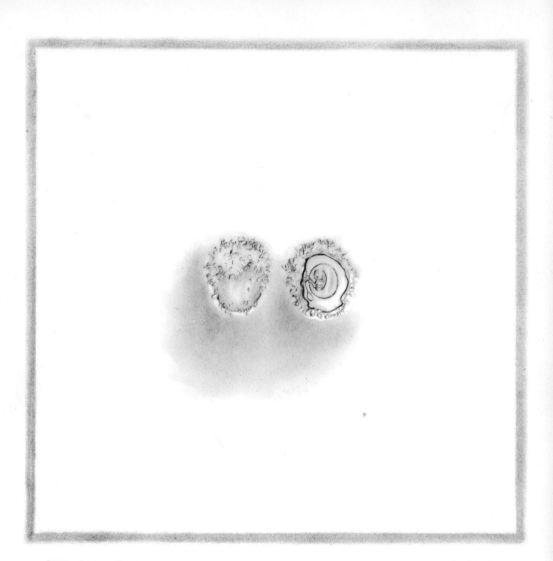

SIX-AND-ONE-HALF-WEEK-OLD HOUSE CLOSED AND OPENED

The sixth, and the seventh, and the eighth weeks passed. Now in these weeks the embryo's house grew from the size of a walnut to the size of an ordinary egg. And in these weeks the sac which held the water grew until it filled the house and covered the walls like a lining. But in these weeks the embryo itself grew faster still. And it unfolded like a

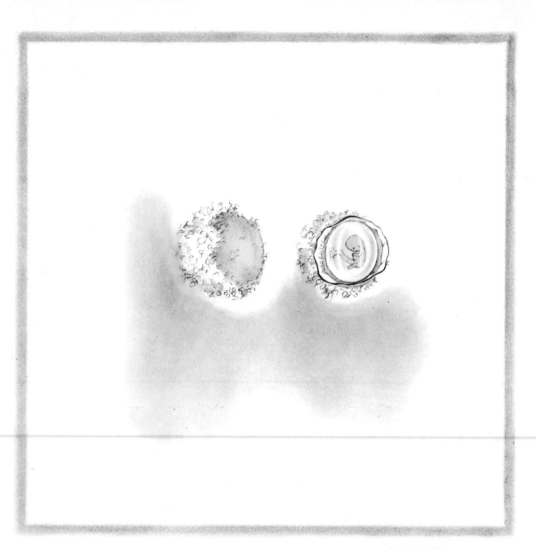

EIGHT-WEEK-OLD HOUSE CLOSED AND OPENED

flower from its bud. It grew and it changed so fast that even the scientists do not agree on exactly which day each thing happened. It grew from the size of a pussy-willow bud to the size of a grandmother's thimble. And out of the curled-up thing like a seed came the form of a baby—the baby it was to be.

And this is how some of it happened:

When the embryo still was no larger than a kernel of rice, or a kernel of wheat, the hole that had burst through its head stretched from side to side like the open mouth of a fish. But it wasn't to be the mouth of a fish. And it went on changing. The edges wrinkled up and started closing like the top of a bag on a string. Then out of the wrinkles and folds came the things they were making. Far apart, on each side came half of a nose and half of a mouth. And up from the things like gills on the neck had come halves for the jaws. So now the embryo had a half of a face on each side of the hole. And as the halves grew they moved closer and closer until they met in the middle. And there they grew together. They did it so neatly only one place, right under the nose, showed like a seam where they had joined. (If you feel with your finger, or look in a glass, you will find those two ridges with a ditch in between,

4 WEEKS	5 WEEKS PLUS	6 WEEKS	6 WEEKS	7 WEEKS
modified after	modified after	modified after	modified after	modified after
Rabl	Rabl Rabl His	Rabl His	Rabl	His His Retzius

IF YOU HAVE A MAGNIFYING GLASS PERHAPS YOU CAN SEE HOW

24

where your own face grew together—when you were the size of a thimble.) And there were lips on the embryo's mouth, and palates inside, which had not yet grown together, and gums, and the beginning of a tongue. And there were cheeks on the embryo's face, and a chin. And the eyes which had been on the sides of its head had moved around to the front. And over and under the eyes there came folds in the skin which made the beginnings of the lids. And up from the first two dents, like gill slits in its neck, came the outside parts for its ears. And the big lump which was the embryo's heart sank down from its chin, leaving room for a neck. So now the head, which was no larger than the tip of your littlest finger, began to straighten up. And there on the front was a face—the face of the baby it was to be. But the eyes were far apart, and the nose was rather flat, and the holes in the nose were plugged with cells.

7 WEEKS PLUS
modified after
Retzius

NEARLY
8 WEEKS
modified after
Hochstetter His

8 WEEKS
modified after
Retzius

9 WEEKS
modified after
Retzius

THE FACE GREW AND CHANGED UNTIL IT WAS THE FACE OF A BABY

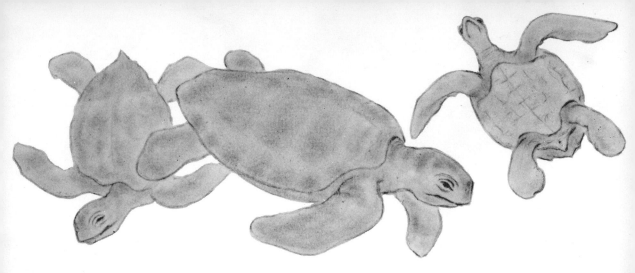

While the face had been growing, other things had been happening too:

At first the buds for the embryo's arms and the buds for its legs flattened out into paddles on the ends, like the flippers or flappers of a sea turtle or a whale. But they were not to be the flippers or flappers of a sea turtle or a whale. And they went on changing as they grew. Then there came ridges on the paddles with hollows between, like the ridges on the flippers of a seal. And there were cushions underneath, like the cushions on the paws of a dog. But these were not to be the paws of a dog nor the flippers of a seal. And the ridges grew out from the paddles and turned into fingers and toes. And there had come bends in the arms and bends in the legs, which made wrists and elbows and ankles and

| 2.5 mm. modified after His | 4.2 mm. modified after Rabl | 6.5 mm. modified after Curtis | 8 mm. modified after His | 9.4 mm. modified after His | 11 mm. modified after His | 14 mm. modified after Rabl |

IF YOU HAVE A MAGNIFYING GLASS PERHAPS YOU CAN SEE

knees. So now the embryo had the arms and the hands and the fingers, and the legs and the feet and the toes of a baby—the baby it was to be. But its arms and its hands and its fingers grew faster at first than its legs and its feet and its toes.

Now the embryo's tail was disappearing, for the growing thighs covered it up. And instead of a sacful of food and a stalk on the place where its stomach was forming, there had come a twisted cord for the embryo to grow on. For embryos cannot eat and they cannot breathe; they must grow like flowers on their stems. So now the roots on the embryo's house all grew on that side where the cord came through, like roots on the end of a stem.

| 15 mm. modified after Jordan and Kindred | 17.3 mm. modified after Hochstetter | 19.5 mm. modified after Hochstetter | 25 mm. modified after Retzius | 28 mm. modified after His |

HOW THE EMBRYO GREW AND UNFOLDED FROM ITS BUD

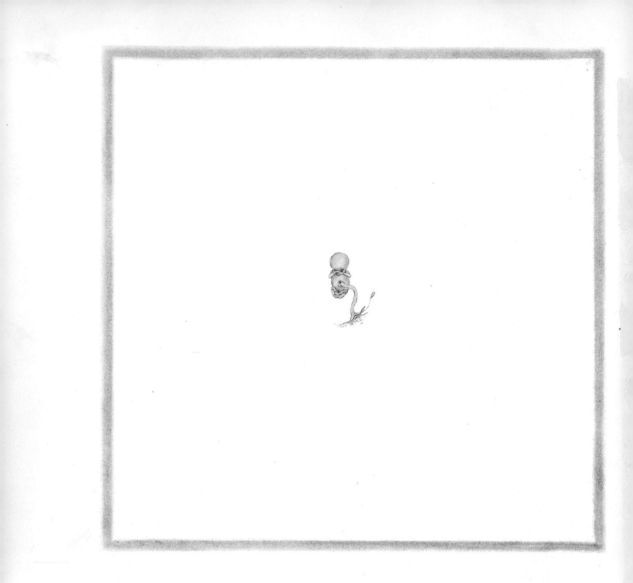

And already the embryo's bones were beginning to harden, but still it looked as fragile as an image made of wax. It was the image of a baby, so small it could hide in a grandmother's thimble, but a baby with all of its fingers, and all of its toes, with two ears and two eyes, and a mouth and a nose. The fingers and toes had no nails, and the eyes had no lids. And there was nothing yet to show whether the baby-to-be was a girl or a boy, for to start with they look just the same.

And this was the end of the eighth week; it was called the end of the second month by the scientists, who count their months by the moon.

(And at this time, when it's so plainly seen what an embryo is to be, the scientists start calling it the *fetus*. But we who do not need to be so wise may still say *embryo*, or call it the *baby-to-be*.)

And the third month passed—the third month by the moon. And the soft walls of the cavity in the mother went on growing. And the sac which was the embryo's house and the sac filled with water grew too. But the embryo inside grew faster still. And now the bud of one small organ grew out, instead of in, which showed that the embryo was a boy. And his arms were growing longer and were lifted up before him, as if to hide his face behind his hands. And now the eyelids covered his eyes and were tightly sealed together so they could not be opened. And on his fingers and toes had come folds in the skin which were buds for the nails. And hidden away in the gums of his mouth there came buds for his teeth, though the buds for his teeth would not grow enough to show until long after he was born. And his legs were growing longer, and he folded them beneath him, like a Buddha in a shrine.

ELEVEN-AND-ONE-HALF-WEEK EMBRYO

And so with bowed head and closed eyes he sat and waited—waited while the buds within him grew into the things they were to be. But not knowing the difference between up and down, the embryo was sitting on his head. (If you turn the book over you can see how he was.)

And the fourth month passed—the fourth month by the moon. At this age all embryos look much alike, with bodies no longer than the heads they bow behind their hands, and eyes sealed shut, and legs that are smaller than their arms. But at this age it can be plainly seen that each one is a self unlike all others. Though still so small you could hold him in the hollow of two hands, the embryo had a look of his own. It could be plainly seen he was himself, and not another. He was the self he would always be, however much he changed and however much he grew —just as you are always you.

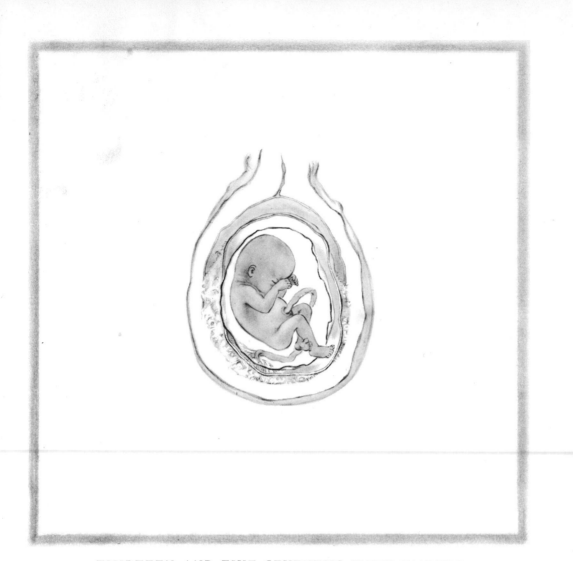

THIRTEEN-AND-FIVE-SEVENTHS-WEEK EMBRYO

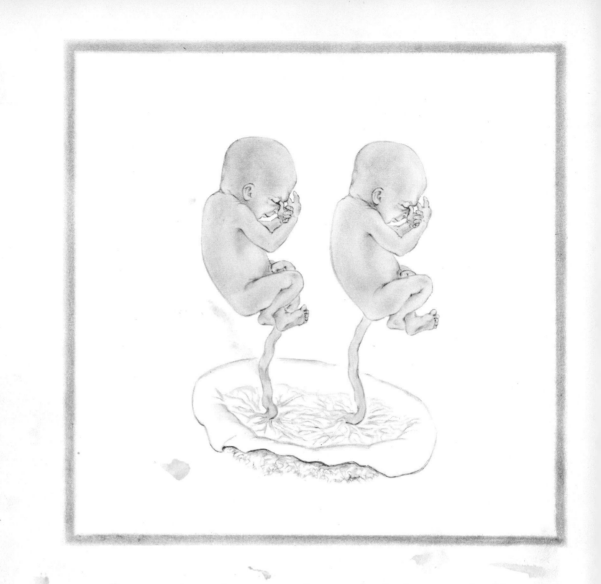

But sometimes there are embryos who look so much alike, even after they are born, that it is difficult to see that each one is a self unlike the other. That is when the cells in a single egg have split into parts after starting to grow, making twins, or triplets, or quadruplets, or quints.

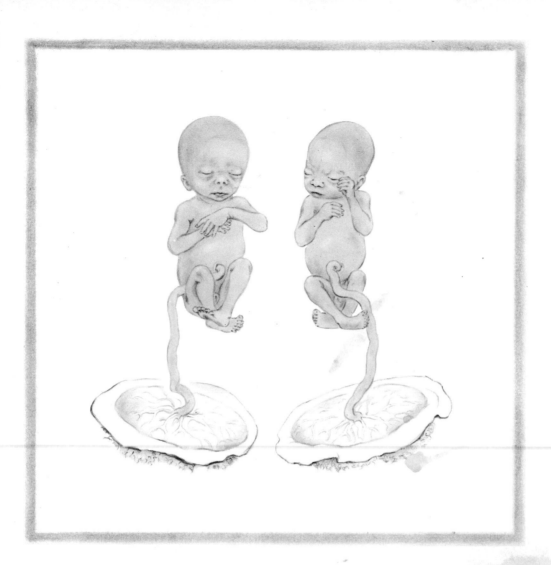

But the twins and triplets and quadruplets who grow from separate eggs look no more alike than brothers and sisters who grow at different times.

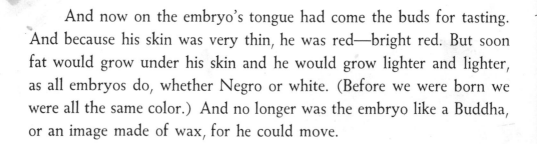

And now on the embryo's tongue had come the buds for tasting. And because his skin was very thin, he was red—bright red. But soon fat would grow under his skin and he would grow lighter and lighter, as all embryos do, whether Negro or white. (Before we were born we were all the same color.) And no longer was the embryo like a Buddha, or an image made of wax, for he could move.

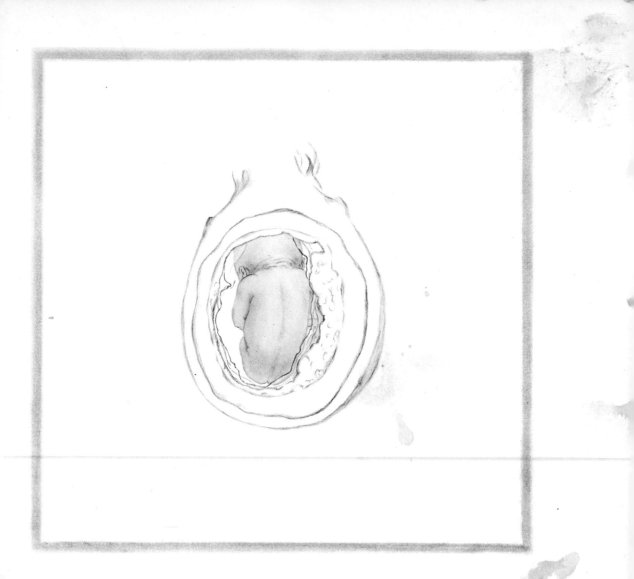

And as the embryo grew he filled the water sac, and the water sac filled the house, and the house filled the cavity in the mother, and the mother could feel it when he bumped against the walls. Sometime, perhaps, you have caught a tiny moth in the cup of your two hands, and although you could not see it, you were sure that it was there, for you could feel the flutter of its wings. Just so the mother felt the flutter of the embryo within her and was sure that it was there.

And the fifth month passed—the fifth month by the moon. And still the embryo grew. He grew faster than his water sac and faster than his house. He grew so fast that he had to curl up like a monkey when it sleeps, and move here and there to find room for his head. And now the roots on the end of the embryo's cord and those parts of the sacs where the roots were growing had matted together into a pad that looked like a basket trying to hold him, but a basket much too small. And on the embryo's body fine hair was appearing, as if he were going to have down like a baby bird or beast. But he was not to be a baby bird or beast, and the hair would stop growing and fall off in the water before he was ready to be born.

And the sixth month passed. Now the mother planned the things that she would need for a baby newborn: something to dress it in, something to wrap it in, something to lay it in where it could sleep. For things like these, it did not matter at all whether the baby-to-be was a girl or a boy. But what could she do for a name, without knowing before if the baby-to-be was a girl or a boy? So the father and young brother and young sister helped her think. They thought of all the names they liked, first names and middle names, names for girls and names for boys. Names are not like other things. You may take them without asking, from anywhere at all, and give them to your baby.

But warm in the water of his sac the embryo himself did not know about such things as names. He did not even know he had a mother and a father and a brother and a sister. Dressed in nothing but a covering like wax, which came from his skin to protect him from long soaking, he waited and he grew.

MORE-THAN-SIX-MONTH EMBRYO

And the seventh month passed, which is twenty-eight weeks. And now, though scarcely longer than his father's shoe, the embryo looked like a very old man, for his skin was too large and wrinkled all over. But the holes in his nose were unplugged. And his eyelids were unsealed and could be opened. And he had the beginnings of eyebrows and lashes and hair on his head. And the buds of all his organs had grown into the things they were to be.

Now when embryos are born at twenty-eight weeks, or maybe at twenty-six (the scientists do not agree), there is a chance for them to live—with incubators to keep them warm and doctors and nurses to watch and take care. But it is not time for them to come; they are too small and weak. The embryos of people must grow forty weeks—ten months by the moon—before they are ready to be born. (Each sort of creature has a time of its own. The embryos of mice grow twenty days before they are ready to be born. But the embryos of elephants must grow twenty months, for the babies of elephants are not so small as the babies of mice.) And so, although the embryo's buds had grown into the things they were to be, it was not time for him to come. He still must wait and grow.

SEVEN-AND-ONE-HALF-MONTH EMBRYO
AS IT WOULD LOOK IF IT COULD BE TAKEN OUT OF ITS HOUSE

And the eighth month passed. And the ninth. And now the embryo was pink and smooth instead of wrinkled and red. And the nails had grown out to the ends of his fingers and to the ends of his toes. And the hair on his head was growing longer. But the hair like down on his body was falling in the water. And still he grew. He grew until he was so squeezed that he scarcely could move. But the mother did not know how squeezed he was, and she began to wonder. She feared the child within her had grown too weak to kick against the walls.

And the tenth month passed—the tenth month by the moon. The time had come. The embryo was ready to be born. And the walls of the cavity in the mother started pushing.

Now how those walls know when to start their pushing—just what it is that tells them—not even the scientists know. And because they do not know they guess and argue, much as other people do. Some say it is the walls themselves grown tired of their burden. Some say it is the child within who has grown too large to stay. Some say it is the roots that have grown too old to do their work. Some say the embryo's head starts pushing through his sacs upon the doorway. Some say it is but habit—that the walls in the mothers of people always *have* pushed at ten months and always will. And some say this, and some say that. But others say it is hormones from pituitary glands—strange messengers that travel through the body doing work so much like magic that the scientists themselves find them hard to understand.

But whatever it is—whatever it was—the time had come, and the walls in the mother started pushing. First they pushed against the sacs

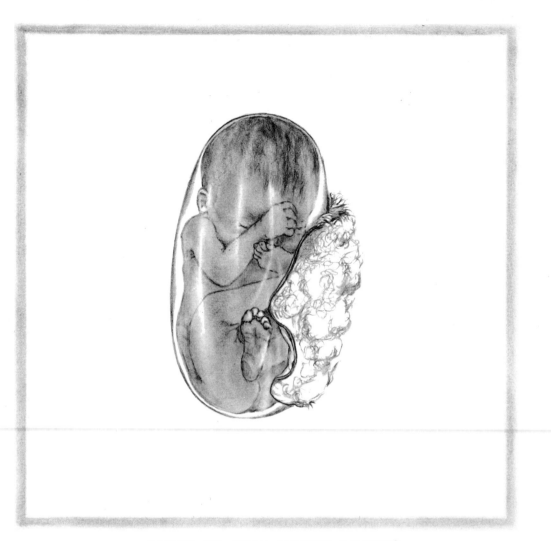

EIGHT-TO-NINE-MONTH EMBRYO

—the sac which was the embryo's house and the sac which held the water. And the sacs burst—burst like the pod of a milkweed when the seeds are ready to fly. Then the walls rested. But soon they would push again.

Now the moving of the walls woke the mother. It was the middle of the night. But she told the baby's father it was time for him to take her to the hospital nearby, where everything was waiting for a baby to be born. And the father called the doctor. And the doctor said he'd be there right away. For doctors all have learned that babies who are struggling to be born do not know about the nighttime and the day, and they come when they are ready.

Now when the walls had rested they began to push again. And this time they were pushing on the baby. They squeezed him and they pushed. They pushed him headfirst through the doorway much too small. They pushed him out into a passage like a hallway much too small. The passage was so small that the soft bones of his head, which had not yet grown together, were pushed one upon the other like a cover on a box. And still the walls pushed on. The baby could not cry because he could not breathe. But the doctor who was listening heard his heart go fast, then slow, then fast, then slow. Must he wither like a flower when it's broken on its stem? Must he die like a fish out of water? Still the walls pushed on. And at last the head came through. The doctor who was waiting let it rest upon his hand, and gently wiped the eyelids with wet gauze. And as the walls pushed on, there came shoulders and arms, and body, and legs.

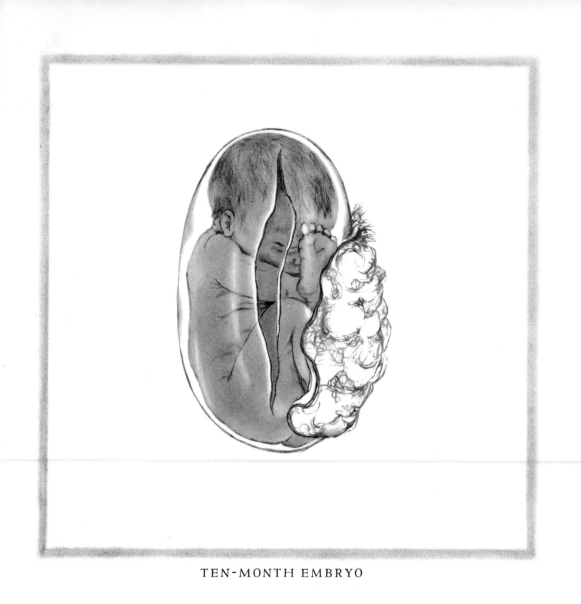

TEN-MONTH EMBRYO

And there he was—a baby newborn—a baby with all of his fingers and all of his toes, with two ears, and two eyes, and a mouth, and a nose. The nurse quickly covered him with warmed towels—all but his face—for he was wet and must not get cold. Then she looked at the clock, for most people want to know what time their baby came. But the doctor was watching the baby. It was time for him to breathe. Why didn't he breathe?

We can't wait for him much longer, thought the doctor. We must try to *make* him breathe. And he slapped the newborn baby on the bottoms of his feet.

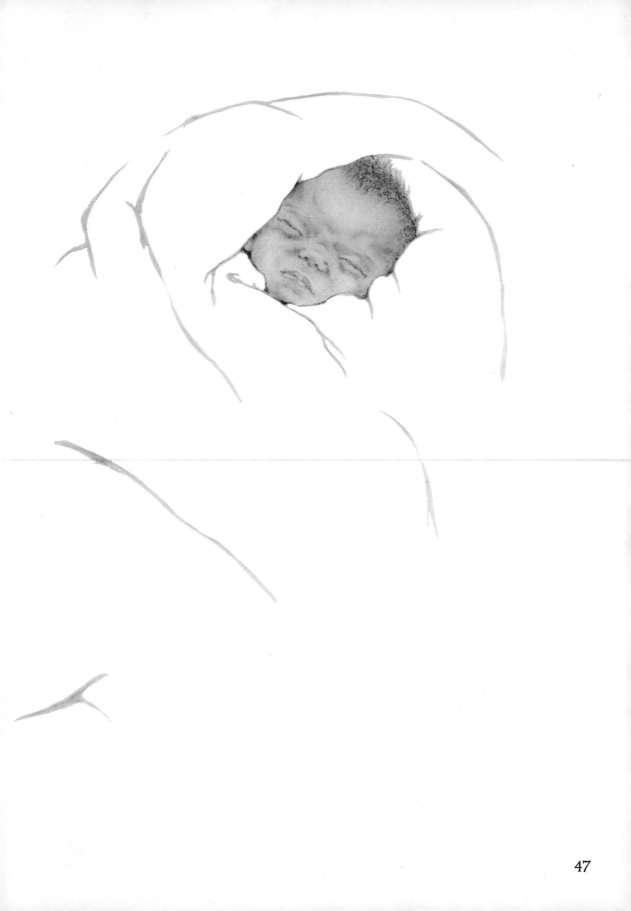

The baby jerked his arms. He gasped. Air filled his lungs. And from his open mouth there came a cry—like a cry of wrath and protest —the *cry of birth!*

"He lives," smiled the doctor.

"He lives," smiled the mother.

"He lives," smiled the nurse—and the father, who was waiting outside.

Now the nurse brought labels and stickers and tags. (The hospitals must have ways to mark their newborn babies so that everyone will know whose child is whose, for babies come as strangers, even to their mothers.) And as the nurse stuck a label on his back and tied a tag on his wrist and one on the wrist of the mother, she read off the number so that everyone could hear—it was the same on all. Everyone could hear it but the baby, for babies just born cannot hear. They must wait until the air has reached the tubes within their ears. Sometimes they wait hours. Sometimes they wait days.

And so the baby could not hear. But he could feel the strange world all about him: air instead of water, space to move instead of sacs to hold him tight. And with every sudden motion of the doctor or the nurse he thought that he was falling. (All newborn babies are afraid that they are falling. They will cling with all their might, like baby monkeys, to anything that touches the insides of their hands. But they do not know to reach for things, nor how to move their arms to find them.)

And now as the baby lay there, breathing for himself, he felt the strangeness of the air against his eyelids and his face. His eyelids moved. They opened. The baby stared into the light. The light hurt his eyes but still he stared, for he did not know to close his lids and shut it out and he did not know what seeing was. He did not even wink when the doctor's hand came near to put in drops. (All doctors must put drops in newborn babies' eyes to clean them and protect them.)

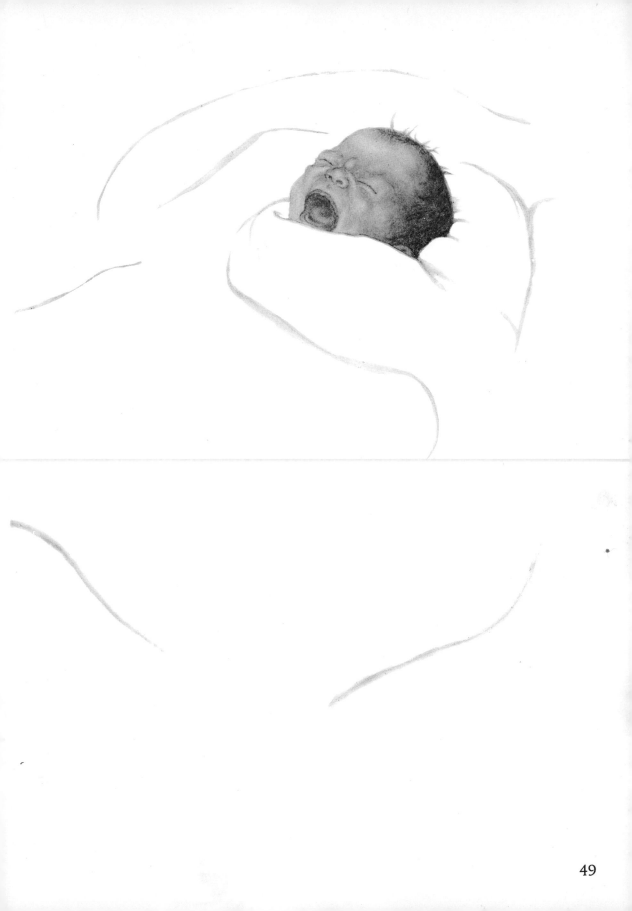

And now the time had come to cut the cord, for there was no more throbbing, which meant that the baby's heart no longer used it. The cord and the roots and the broken sacs had finished their work and would be thrown away. So the doctor tied a tape around the cord, close to the baby's belly. The baby squirmed and kicked and punched, for a cord is like your hair—it pulls when it is tied, although you cannot feel it when it's cut. Then the doctor cut it off with his scissors and he put a bandage on the piece that was left to keep it dry and clean. In a week or ten days it would wither and drop off like the stem of an apple, leaving only a hole to show where it had been.

Then the doctor examined the baby, for he wanted to be sure that everything had grown the way it should. Then he lifted him up in a blanket and gave him to the nurse. The nurse had a basket ready with warm water bags and blankets. She laid him on his side with his head down lower than his feet, to clear his nose and throat of anything that bothered. And just as she let go, the baby sneezed. Then she covered him with a blanket and shaded his eyes from the lights, and she took him away. She took him to the room where they care for the babies.

In the room where they care for the babies, which was warm, with no drafts or bright lights, he felt himself lifted from the basket and taken from the blankets, though he didn't know what they were. He was laid on something hard. The hard thing sank beneath him. He jerked his arms and cried—he was sure that he was falling. But the nurse went on balancing the scales to see how much he weighed and she wrote it on his record. He weighed nearly seven pounds. Then she laid him on the table and measured, with his legs stretched out as straight as they would go. He was nineteen inches long.

Now she daubed him with warm oil and rubbed him with cotton to take off that covering like wax which had protected him from soaking

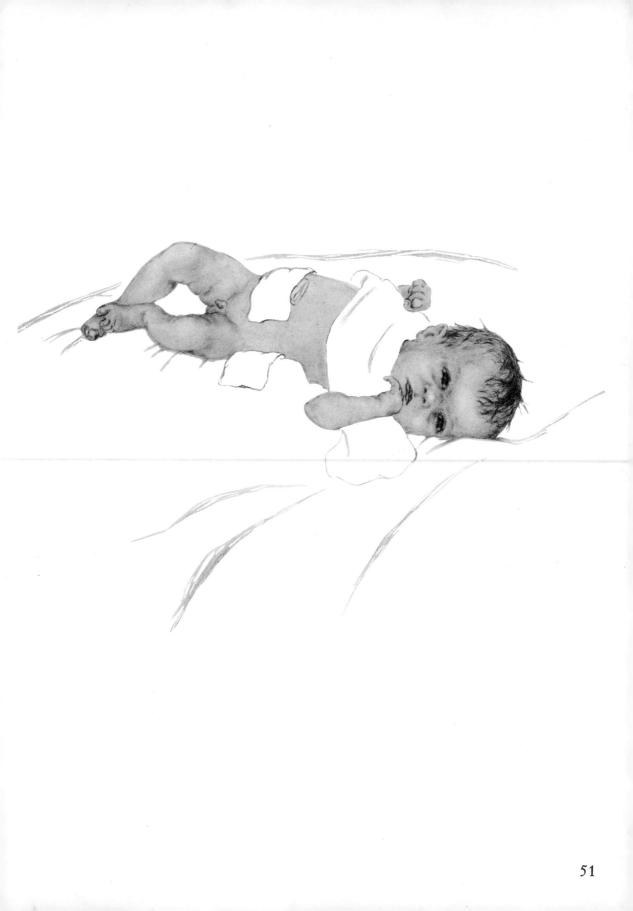

in the water—the *vernix caseosa,* as the scientists call it. The baby squirmed. He kicked. He cried with all his might. For the soft pink skin of babies just born is very tender—pink when they are born, but red a few hours later. Then the nurse pressed a pad of ink against the palms of his hands, and pressed his hands against the record. For palm prints are another way for hospitals to know whose child is whose. And she took his footprints, too, to please his mother. Then she sponged him with soap and warm water. First she laid him on his back. Then she laid him face down with his nose against the table. He had to squirm and work and struggle to turn and lift his head enough to breathe. And he clung with hands and knees, for he thought that he was falling. (Babies just born cannot lift their heads at all when laid upon their backs. But when laid upon their faces they will turn and lift their heads enough to breathe.)

And now his clothing: First the nurse sewed a bellyband over his bandage, and put on a shirt and some diapers. Then she pulled the nightdress up over his feet. As she reached for an arm to pull it through the sleeve, something touched the baby on the inside of his hand. It was something to hold on to. He grabbed it and he clung. The nurse had to loosen his thin fingers to make him let go of her thumb. And when she had sewed on the nightdress and wrapped him in a blanket, she gave him a spoonful of water—but she gave it from a bottle, for newborn babies want to suck —and watched to see that he could swallow. Then she took him to the nursery and laid him in a crib.

In the nursery there were rows and rows of cribs with babies in them and all the cribs had labels to tell whose child was whose. Some of the babies were crying—each one with a cry of its own. But all of the crying together made very little noise. It was like the peeping and the calling and the whining and the bleating of baby birds and beasts. But most of the babies were sleeping—for newborn babies are never long awake. As if they would escape the strangeness of the world that is about them, they sleep—and sleep—and sleep. And so as the baby lay there, snug in the blankets of his crib, his eyelids drooped and closed. He too would sleep.

When morning came young brother and young sister learned of the birth of the baby. They hurried through their breakfasts without caring what they ate. Then they ran to their neighbors and their friends, for they wanted everyone to know they had a baby brother. But how could they wait so many days to see him? They would have to wait until the mother brought him home because the hospital had rules about young children and would not let them visit. Each night when the father came home they asked him questions, and more questions. The father told them that the baby looked too old, too old for one so young; he looked like a very old man. And most of the time he just slept in his crib in the room that was full of new babies, behind a glass wall, and all of the babies looked old. Young brother and young sister were wishing they could see it—a room that was full of new babies. But most of all they wanted to see their *own*. Would the day never come when their mother would bring him home! They counted the days. They counted and they waited.

Now there was a law in the state where the baby was born that all births must be reported, for most governments of peoples like to count their newborn babies to know how many and what kind. Then should they ever want to know the age of any child they can find it in their records. And so to the rooms in the city hall where the records are kept, there came by mail a report of the baby from the doctor, and a clerk who was writing in large books at a desk copied off the day, and the place where the baby was born, and the name of the mother, and the name of the father. And he copied off the name of the baby—the names that the mother and the father and young brother and young sister had decided they liked best for a boy. Then he filled in other spaces and copied the name of the doctor.

And at other desks, and in other towns, and in other lands, other clerks were writing. For every day of every year in every land more babies come. They do not know to what nor why, but still they come—and come—and come.

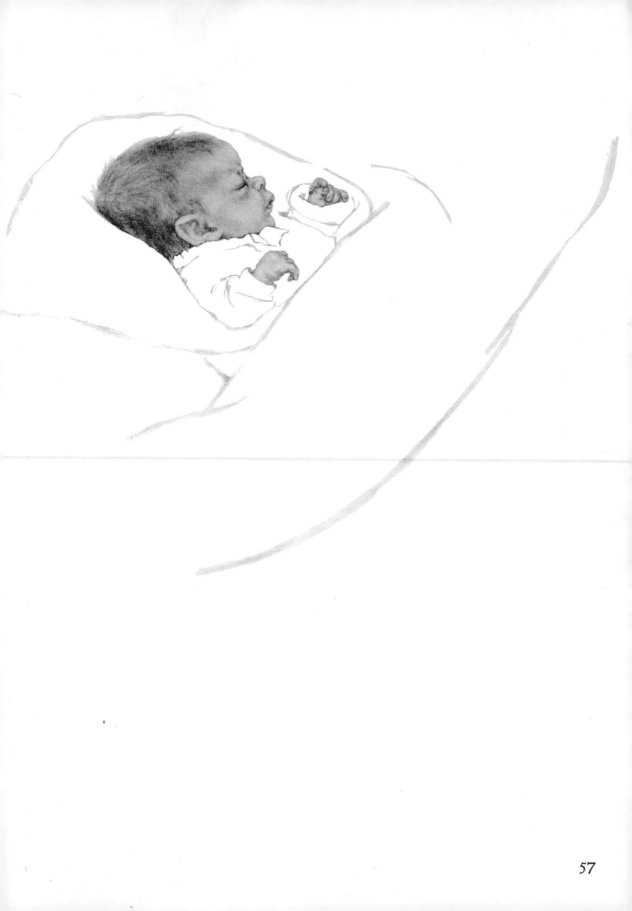

At first, when the baby was brought home, the children could see nothing but his blankets, for he was all wrapped up in a bundle. Then they saw one eye and a very small nose and when the blankets were loosened they saw his two hands, and all of the fingers were moving. Then they saw the rest of his face and the hair on his head. His face did look wrinkled and old, as the father had said. But they liked it anyway. And now the eyelids opened and they saw his eyes—eyes so dark that even the whites were blue. They talked to him, and they were sure that he was listening, for he stared into their faces. But he scowled as he stared, as if he could not understand and he seemed so sad—so sad—so sad. Perhaps he did not like it here, and did not want to stay? But all at once he closed his eyes and yawned. He yawned so hard that it sounded like a sigh. And everybody laughed—it was so funny.

Then young brother and young sister sat down in low chairs and placed their arms as they were told, for they were going to hold him, first one and then the other. When young sister felt the wiggling through the blanket and the clothing, she held her breath and was afraid to move. But when young brother felt the wiggling through the blanket and the clothing, he held on tight and grinned. Then the baby was laid in his crib. But his eyes would not stay open. And before he had finished his milk he was asleep.

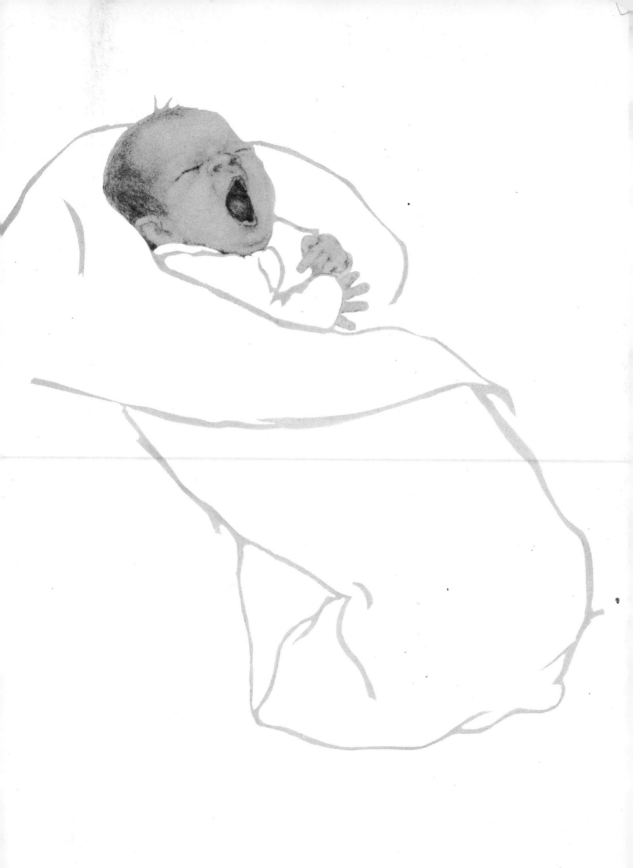

In the morning young brother and young sister watched the baby in his bath. He no longer had a bandage on his belly, for the cord had fallen off, leaving only the hole to show where it had been. And so he was bathed in his tub. But he didn't like to have his head washed—he punched and squirmed and tried to get away. And he didn't want to open up his fists to have the fuzz from the blankets washed out. And once, without warning, he kicked so hard that he splashed them all over. But what he seemed to like best was a chance to stretch when the bathing was over. Laid on a blanket without any clothes he stretched and stretched and stretched, like any other baby animal. But then he shivered and had to be dressed.

Day after day young brother and young sister visited the baby at his crib. They talked to him, and shook their heads, and wrinkled up their faces, and sometimes rattled paper to amuse him. But when they rattled paper they did it very gently, for new babies are afraid of sudden noises. They will jump, and sometimes cry, at the dropping of a pencil.

Day after day the baby watched them and he listened. He learned to turn his head to find their faces, and would follow them with his eyes. But he looked so sad as he watched and as he listened, as if he could not understand. His eyes seemed always to be asking where he was, and what he was, and why.

Day after day, when the children were sent to their play, they lingered in the hallway. They sat down on the steps outside. They dug holes in the ground with their heels. *Would he never learn to like it here? Would he never want to stay?*

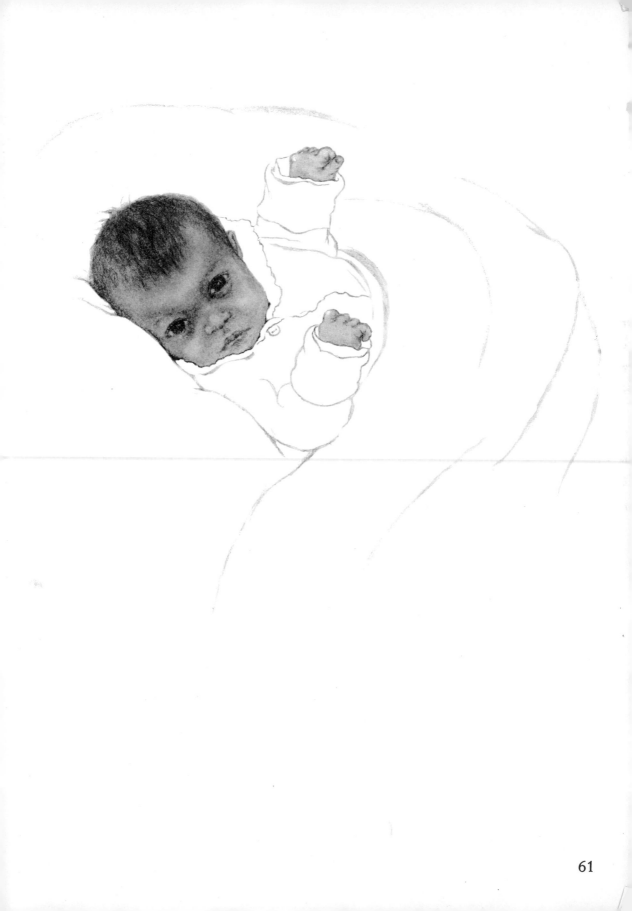

A few weeks passed. There came another day and again the children visited the baby at his crib. They shook their heads and wrinkled up their faces. They made up words and talked to him in sounds that had no meaning. The baby turned his head. He watched them, and he listened. All at once he seemed to understand the things that had no meaning. And he liked them. They were funny!

"Come!" called the children to their mother. "Come!"

Then the mother saw it too, for he did it again and again.

Now on this day, when the children were sent to their play, they raced through the hallway. They leaped from the steps outside. They tumbled and fell, trying to stand on their heads. Then they rolled on the grass and lay there, laughing, with their faces to the sky. *He had smiled—their new baby! He could smile!*